BERNARD BRIGGS

BERNARD BRIGGS, scrapman and famous all-round sportsman was on his way back from picking up some scrap, when—

Stone the crows! I'm being dive-bombed!

That idiot has turned me into a hedge-hog.

Help! I'm stuck in my safety harness!

Then it ain't all that safe then, is it? Hang on, mate!

B BRIGGS GENERAL DEALER

Out you come.

What is it? One of them hang-gliding things?

Yes, it's a hang-glider and as far as I'm concered it can go hang!

Tell you what, mate. I'm a scrap merchant. If you're really getting rid of it, I'll take it off your hands. How much?

You can have it for nothing, chum—and good riddance.

Is this hang-gliding lark easy, then?

No way! It's bloomin' hard and dangerous too, mate. Take my advice, keep your feet on the deck!

But Bernard was determined to have a go. Next day—

This hang-gliding lark can't be all that hard. I'll have a go from the top of this slope.

Here goes!

A perfect two point landing! This is great fun!

Get off my land, you lout! I'll have you arrested for trespassing!

Oh, oh! It's Sir George again! I didn't know it was your land! Sorry, squire!

Blimey, looks like I've even got to get permission to land!

Reg was waiting for Bernard when he got back to his bike—

Hi, Bernard. I saw you come down—and I saw Sir George. He owns most of the land around here and he's also the local magistrate. Watch him.

I'll do that, Reg. I reckon he's got it in for me!

There is a duration contest next weekend, open to all. Why don't you have a go, Bernard?

A duration contest! Stay up as long as you can, eh? I like the sound of that!

On the Saturday—

Briggs! What the blazes are you doing here?

Same as you, mate, only I aim to do it better!

Don't take this fellow's entry, Reg!

We must, Sir George! It's a Sailway Society competition, open to anyone!

7

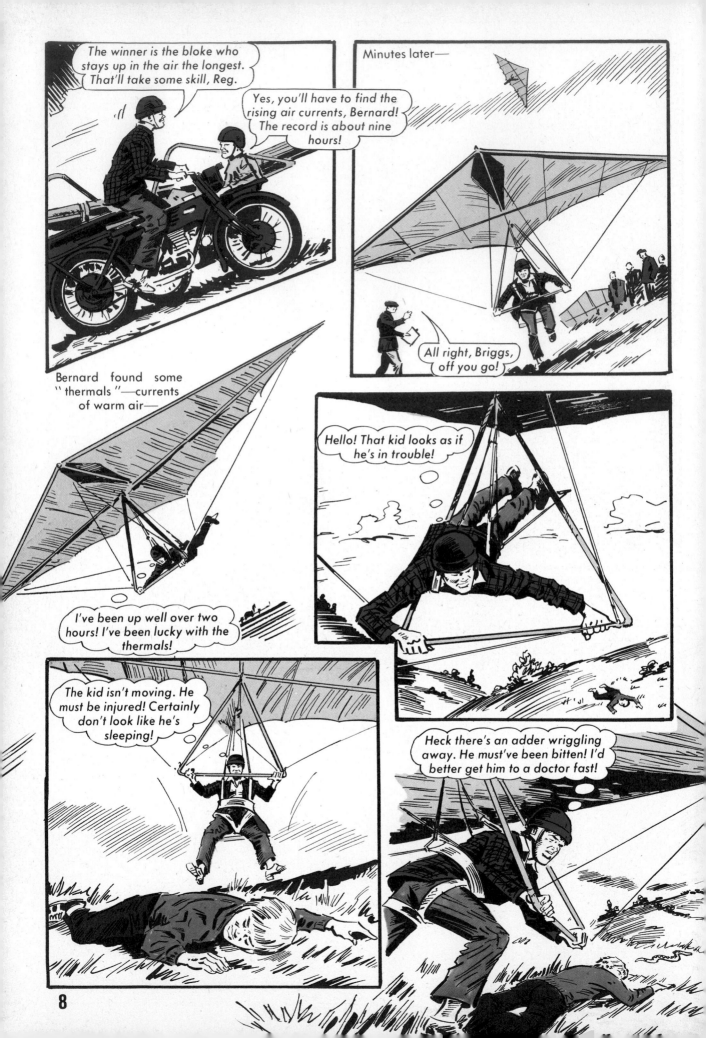

9

You deliberately damaged my car! You'll go to jail for this, Briggs! I'll see to it.

Okay, Sir George, but get this kid to hospital first. He's been bitten by an adder!

It's Geoffrey, my son! Is he dead?

No, he isn't, but he will be if you don't step on it!

Is he still breathing?

Concentrate on the road, mate! We want to get to hospital, not land in it!

An hour later—

My son is out of danger, thanks to you, Briggs! Oh, by the way. You also won the duration contest! You were airborne for two hours, 48 minutes.

WARDS 1-10

Great news, mate, about your son and my contest win!

A week later—

This is super! When I grow up I'm going to be a scrap-man like you, Bernard!

Fair enough, Geoff! I could use a partner!

Well, I'm now a member of the club and official scrap gatherer for the whole of Sir George's estate. And I've won my first hang-gliding cup. There's never a dull moment!

THE END

10

THE FOX—MASTERMIND OF DISGUISE AND ESCAPE!
HIS MISSION—SMUGGLING FUGITIVES OUT OF THE IRON CURTAIN STATE OF ASCOVIA!
HIS OPPONENTS—THE VIPERS-ASCOVIAN SECRET POLICE OF COMMISSAR ERST RILLA!
What's that? It's coming in high over the wall!
ESCAPE
It looks like a flying saucer!
Idiot! There's no such thing!
Don't shoot at it, you fool. It might be important!
It's vanishing from sight! Someone inform headquarters!

At Headquarters, Chief Commissar Rilla was informed of the sighting—

WHAT? Give a general alert! Anything coming from the other side of the wall could mean danger. I want that thing found—UNDERSTAND?

Y-Yes, Herr Commissar!

Meanwhile, at some open ground in the centre of the city, the Fox was waiting—

Here it comes! Bring the truck forward, Jan!

Right away, Fox!

Our friends in the West have done us proud! This contains another passport out of Ascovia!

Minutes later—

Oh-oh! The Vipers —Rilla's Secret Police. Looks like they want us to stop!

14

16

Seems to be heading for the Lower East Side.

SCRAP CAR DEALER

He turned in here. Must have gone through the wrecking yard.

I'm blocked. Better back up.

Now I'm boxed in!

Oh-oh! Looks like I'm gonna fly.

21

That fixes the Frenchman's two friends.

Now to stake out this yard till he comes back.

HERALD
GOVERNOR IN GOLF CHARITY

So that's why the Frenchman is off golfing. Wagh! My nearest help is Tim James over at the Navy Yard.

Tim, I'll be crossing the East River by the Williamsburg Bridge. You'd better have a 'copter waiting—unless you want a dead Governor!

Jay got his helicopter.

The golf course is at Silver Lake Park. That's down in Richmond.

There it is. Now to look for the kind of spot the Frenchman would pick, for one of his long shots.

COARSE GOLF

You've seen Mantracker foil a golf course murder bid. Here are some other odd things that have happened on golf courses throughout the world.

Golfer A.W. Good took a mighty swipe at his second shot to the 6th hole on the Lewes golf course. He overbalanced and fell head first into a sheep trough full of water.

A Harrogate golfer, delighted at holing a 20 yard putt on the last green, threw his club in the air. It came down and k.o'd his unfortunate partner.

Myrl G. Henmore was chased and eventually run down by his motorised caddy car on Toronto golf course.

In the 1972 Singapore Open Championship, Jimmy Stewart found his ball guarded by a ten foot cobra at the third hole.

One armed J.W. Perrett killed sea gulls with his second shots to the 1st and 2nd holes in the same round at Troon.

Dozy Danny

"DOZY" DANNY DEAN was a member of the England team in Mexico City for the World Youth Cup. Dozy was living up to his nickname.

Where's Dean? If he's still in his bed—

I'll wake up that man and see if he's seen him, Boss!

Why, it's Dozy Danny. Ha! Ha! You'll doze anywhere, won't you, Dozy?

Step on it, Speedy Gonzales! We have a semi final to play!

England were playing Holland in the first semi-final. The second was between Mexico, the home country, and West Germany.

Would you believe it, Danny's sleeping again. Wake up, Danny! We're at the stadium!

Don't worry. He never sleeps on the football field, mate!

Dozy started the game like a fire-cracker.

Throughout the first half England mounted attack after attack but the Dutch defence stood firm. In the second half the Dutch were still hemmed into their own half but their keeper was in tremendous form and even Dozy Danny couldn't beat him.

With five minutes to go the Dutch defence was forcing Danny to the right. Suddenly—

A quick stop, and—

I've caught 'em on the wrong foot.

GOAL!

The Dutch team panicked. Danny's magic footwork took him through the defence again.

Beat you again, mate.

There was no time to restart the game.

I've heard the other result, lads. We play Mexico in the final. Ta-t-a-ta-ta-ta-ta-ta.

That night, outside the England team's hotel.

Do something! Call the police! How can my players sleep in this din?

I am so sorry, senor. The police, they can do nothing. The fans, they do no harm.

They plan to keep us awake. Oh well, might as well use the time.

I don't see any keep off the grass signs. So I'll have a bit of ball practice!

Danny dribbled the ball in and out amongst the flower beds.

Then suddenly—

27

We are in luck. We have captured the famous goal scorer!

Later.

What's the idea, chum? If I've been kidnapped for ransom, better forget it. Who'd pay money for me?

Oh no, senor! You are honoured guest—till after the game!

Danny was a prisoner in a luxury ranch house.

You must eat, senor. Chilli con carne. Very fine Mexican food.

No chance of fish and chips, I suppose? Okay, Jeeves, pile it on.

Wow! Garoooh! This stuff's red-hot!

Danny dived through an open window and made for a fountain.

I'm on fire!

You wish a drink, senor?

No way! If it's as hot as your food, it'll burn my tonsils off!

Later.

Can I get you anything, senor?

Si, get me a football.

Danny practised his ball work, never letting the ball touch the floor.

Beats loafing around!

You disturb my siesta, Senor Danny. You are not dozy now, no?

If I'm bothering you, mate. I'll go outside.

Danny was allowed out into the courtyard under guard.

That posh geezer must be the guy that had me kidnapped. Wonder if he's connected with football in some way?

Danny showed his guards a new kind of hat dance.

Mexican hat dance —Danny Dean version!

As the days passed and Danny made no attempt to escape, the guards became less vigilant.

The final is tonight. After Mexico wins, take Senor Dozy well away from here and release him.

The final's tonight! Now's the time to make my move!

Siesta time, and Danny's only guard was half asleep.

Aahhh!

Have a siesta, senor. A bash with a guitar is as good as a lullaby!

Adios, amigo.

Good! He hasn't seen through my disguise.

A handy bus. Hope I've enough small change for the fare!

The bus was bound for Mexico City.

Oh gimme a home where the buffalo roam . . .

Dressed as he was, Danny could not get into the football stadium. He waited for the England team bus.

There he is! Dozy's made it for the final!

Dozy was through, straight from the kick-off, but—

A few minutes later.

33

34

But, as they approached the house—

Hey! Look what we got here, guys—the two cutest cops in Las Minola!

Well, well! The property values around here just took a nose-dive, Man! We oughta tell the Health Department about this garbage over on the West Side!

This chain'll button your lip, fuzz-man!

Too slow, buddy-boy! Into 'em, Clancy!

UNH!

You guys've had it! And your pal's runnin'!

In the lift up to Packer's apartment—

Those punks weren't there by accident, Man. They were covering someone visiting these apartments!

Yeah! Someone who couldn't afford more reliable bodyguards!

Midge Runnett! And he's coming out of Al's apartment!

Comin' out a lot richer than he went in, too!

Hold it right there, Midge! Where did you get this money?

Hey, cool it, Clancy. You ain't got no right to manhandle a law-abiding citizen like this!

35

Phew! It's safe!

Thanks, Midge. We guessed you'd go straight for this document. That's the one thing you wouldn't want to lose above all else.

You were fooled, Midge! There's no fire—only the smoke from this canister.

Now you disappear, Midge. You'd be going behind bars if we didn't want to keep this whole mess quiet. Consider yourself lucky. But one squeak from you and you'll go away for a long time. Is that clear?

Y—yeah, Clancy. You ain't gonna see me around—I promise!

Later, back at Packer's apartment—

You got the document back! I don't know how to thank you, Clancy.

Forget it, Al. But when Midge tells Macey about this, Macey's going to realise that he doesn't have any kind of hold over you. It could force him to make another move, so keep us informed.

Midge was already in touch with the Governor—

I'm sorry, boss, but those two cops grabbed the paper. They only let me go because I could've made a big noise.

Then you'll have to kill Packer. I don't want that loudmouth in my hair again!

In Macey's office—

Arrange to meet him tomorrow night at one a.m. in Grover Park. Tell him to go on foot and not to have anyone with him. I'll meet you after you've iced him and see you're well paid.

37

But Midge had ideas of his own. The next evening, he slipped into the TV studio car-park and found Al Packer's car—

This bomb'll go off when Packer accelerates over 45 m.p.h. I'll tell him to come by car. Then I'll meet Macey at Grover Park and tell him it's all over.

Later, Midge rang Al Packer at the studio—

Meet me at one a.m. in Grover Park, Packer. I'll tell you who was behind this set-up. But it'll cost you.

It's a deal, Midge. I'll be there.

Packer called Clancy right away. Within half an hour, they were at the T.V. studios—

What do you think, Clancy? Is it some kind of trick?

Could be, Al. We'll stick around and take you to the Park in our car. We'll drop you off and then watch you good and close.

But at that moment, Macey was putting his own double-cross into action! And that meant stealing Al Packer's car!

Midge could bleed me dry with what he has on me. This way I can get rid of Packer and Midge in one go. I run down Midge with Packer's car and then ditch it. Those cops know Midge was squeezing Packer so he'd have good reason to kill Midge!

I'll drive nice and steady to the Park and hang around until I see Midge appear. Then—wham! No more Midge and no more Packer!

At one a.m. in Grover Park—

Hello Midge!

PACKER! But—but didn't you drive here?

Midge looks surprised to see Al. What's he up to?

Just then—

That's your car, Packer! But who's driving it?

It's Macey! STOP! YOU'LL KILL US ALL!

HE'S ACCELERATING! HE'S TRYING TO KILL US!

Come on! Get out of the way!

As the car hit Midge—

My bomb's exploding! AAGH!

Looks like Macey planned a double-cross and it boomeranged on him, Man!

And he took Midge with him, Clancy. One way and another, this case is all wrapped up!

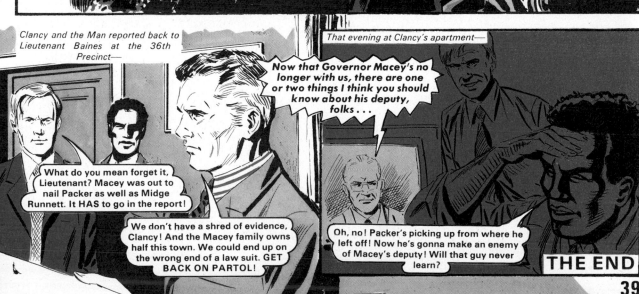

Clancy and the Man reported back to Lieutenant Baines at the 36th Precinct—

What do you mean forget it, Lieutenant? Macey was out to nail Packer as well as Midge Runnett. It HAS to go in the report!

We don't have a shred of evidence, Clancy! And the Macey family owns half this town. We could end up on the wrong end of a law suit. GET BACK ON PATROL!

That evening at Clancy's apartment—

Now that Governor Macey's no longer with us, there are one or two things I think you should know about his deputy, folks . . .

Oh, no! Packer's picking up from where he left off! Now he's gonna make an enemy of Macey's deputy! Will that guy never learn?

THE END

39

THE HAMMER OF VULKAN

You cannot take my men! I cannot spare any! The Russians have broken through!

That is not your concern, Colonel. The Army may not question the orders of the SS! This is by command of SS Brigadefuhrer Eikhart.

THE Eastern Front, 1944. Brigadefuhrer Eikhart of the dreaded SS Field Police had devised a typical Nazi trick to destroy his sworn enemies, the Hammer of Vulkan. There were a small group who, sickened at the merciless methods of the SS, had escaped from a Punishment Battalion, one of the suicide groups set up the by the SS in a desperate attempt to stem the the Russian onslaught.

A few days later, the men of Vulkan were in the forest.

Russian cossacks! Those poor blokes in the sledges don't stand a chance, Prof.

Let's get down and help our comrades, Max.

Keep shooting, Max.

I don't think we can save the sledge men, Prof.

My arm!

I got him, Hans.

Die, Germanski . . .ugh!

The men of Vulkan decided to carry the fight to the SS. If they could not get Eikhart to come out into the open they would go in and get his officers, in their own headquarters

In through the wire, lads. That's the place we're going to hit. Over the fence, Prof.

By the time we've finished, Eikhart will have to come out here—he'll be the only SS officer left!

There's an SS officer —what the . . . ?!!!

Ugh!

Someone shot him! Let's get out of here. The guard is roused.

There they are! The killers—

Get through the fence, Prof. I'll keep these swine occupied!

Who fired that shot? I'll ram the weapon down his throat. He nearly got us all killed!

Whoever it was, that was a perfect bit of shooting.

Two days later, the Vulkan set an ambush for other SS officers.

Here they come! Get ready!

Just then . . .

I saw a flash of light—up there! Someone using binoculars?

Or telescopic sights! It could be our phantom marksman!

The sniper struck.

Urgh!

We're being attacked from the trees!

They've turned and gone! We'll never catch them.

Stop! We're going to have a word with our sniper friend up there.

Friend, we just want to know what your game is. We were about to kill those SS when you struck.

My brother was murdered by the SS Field Police. Now I'm paying them back.

That night.

That must be his camp fire. Be careful. We're dealing with an expert.

But he seems to be on our side.

There's no one here. I smell an ambush . . . A bullet!

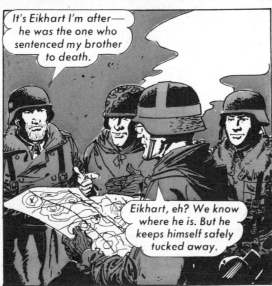

It's Eikhart I'm after—he was the one who sentenced my brother to death.

Eikhart, eh? We know where he is. But he keeps himself safely tucked away.

Eikhart never makes a move unless he's got his bodyguard with him. But a sniper like you should be able to get a crack at him—with a little help from us.

45

Later, the Vulkan raided a SS post.

Tell Eickhart exactly what I've told you. And remember, my friend is a very good shot—and eager to prove it!

SS officers are my favourite targets.

One of the Vulkan has surrendered, Herr Eikhart—a Wolfgang Keppler. He wants to make a deal with you personally, Herr Brigadefuhrer.

Why pick me?

You are the youngest, Little Wolf, and in their eyes that makes you the weakest.

Eikhart's response was typical.

Promise him anything, if he will lead us to the other swine. Then we'll shoot him along with the rest.

Get a move on, driver! I want to reach them before nightfall.

The Vulkan were in ambush, again.

While we're waiting I'll finish off those SS men—just like they did my brother.

We don't shoot unarmed men—even though they are SS!

Here they come! Eikhart's brought an army with him.

You know what to do. We've got to split them up, so our sniper friend will have a clear shot.

It's a trap!

It's me they're after! You must protect this car!

46

THEY FOUGHT ON THE RUSSIAN FRONT

12.7 mm 1938 HEAVY MACHINE-GUN
The first Soviet heavy machine-gun to be produced in quantity, it had a firing rate of 540-600 rounds a minute, fed by a 50-round metal-link belt and was standard equipment throughout the war.

SOVIET PPSh SUBMACHINE-GUN
One of the simplest guns ever made, it fired the standard 7.62 mm. cartridge at a rate of 900 per minute. Most of the five million produced during the war were only able to fire automatically. It was crude, but effective!

T.34/76
Russia's most famous "battle wagon". This 1942 model, with a crew of 4, had a 76 mm. gun and two machine guns. Regarded as the best tank of its time, it saw service throughout the war, in various forms. One of the few faults was the single, large turret hatch.

122mm. TYPE 31/37 HOWITZER
Loaded and ready to fire, this heavy artillery piece weighed 15,500 lb. It had a range of 22,000 yards and, with the steep barrel-angle, virtually lobbed shells on to the enemy.

That stuff don't half make you sleepy!

It's working.

They do not know they've been drugged! We had to do it for the sake of our village.

The headman moved away from the Britishers—

I will call the Japanese! We promised co-operation!

Otherwise, they destroy our village and kill us! It is the Japanese way!

Tell them to try to remove the enemy's weapons and ammunition. We move out now!

We take as many as we can alive!

Slave labour is scarce! Prisoners work till they die!

Meanwhile—

Where's old Bozzler got to? Maybe I'll see him from up here!

Perishin' Japs! And they're heading for the same village as our lads were headin' for.

I gotta get there first an' warn our lads!

Old Bozzler's let me down. I could do with some help!

I've beat the Japs, but not by much!

Bert reached the village—

Blimey! Something's wrong! The villagers have our lads' guns! I'll have to be wary!

When the Japs reached the village—

We did as you ordered! The British are drugged!

You were wise!

Take the curs!

We've been betrayed! Aaah, my head!

Resist and you die! You are prisoners!

53

They're with us!

Bert and his bear! Bozzler wasn't killed after all!

Good ol' Bozzler—thump 'em, boy!

I don't believe in miracles, but . . .

No miracle—just Bozzler! The Burmese boys don't like bears bein' killed!

They think Bozzler's a sort o' spirit and he be on our side. 'E got 'em over their fear o' the Japs!

Lucky for us, eh, sergeant?

VERY lucky, sir!

It ain't done that before! Looks like she's coming in to land. But that's a swampy area she's heading for. If she comes down there she'll be in bad trouble.

If that baby's coming in to land, I want to be there!

Chad hurled his car in pursuit of the dropping space-ship. But as he got closer—

It's turning to take off again! I'll be burned-up in that blazing jet-stream!

It's set my car on fire! But I must get some pictures—I MUST!

Whoever they are, they must've realised that the swamp was a bad landing-ground! But at least I got some good shots of that thing! Now, if I can borrow that farmer's truck, I'll get this stuff straight to my paper.

I warned you, Chad! No more crazy 'out-of-this-world' stunts! Men from space indeed! You must think I'm some kind of idiot!

You don't have to take my word—there's a camera full of evidence right there in front of you! And while you're having the film developed, let me take you to where the thing almost landed. It burned up my car!

This don't mean a thing, Chad. That could've been a simple scrub fire and your car got caught up in it. You've cooked-up evidence for your wild stories before.

What does it take to convince you? Sure I've hoaxed you before, but this is the real thing. When you see those pictures, you'll be convinced.

But, back at the newspaper office . . .

So THAT'S what you call evidence, huh? All we've got here is a few pictures of the SUN! Over-exposed and out of focus! Now get out of my office and bring me a story of the President's visit or you're fired!

Of all the lousy luck! The light and heat must've ruined the film. I'll never convince him now.

But Chad wasn't to be beaten.

The President is due in about two hours. I'd better get myself into some kind of vantage point. Hey! Wait a minute! This could be just the angle to get the police involved. And if THEY start moving I've got a story . . . I'll go get that farmer!

Later, at the police station . . .

You've got two eye-witnesses and a burned-out car, officer. Are you prepared to ignore this with the President's visit imminent? Is it coincidence that the space-ship tried to land just hours before the President's visit?

I guess it wouldn't hurt to take a look at that spot. Let's go.

But Chad was to get a bigger story than he'd ever dreamed of! A little later—

In the name of—! Look at THAT!

And that HAS to be real, officer— or we're sharing the same hallucination! Now what do you say?

This is an emergency. An alien craft is landing two miles south-east of town. Get troops and tanks to the vicinity immediately. This is a red-alert. The President is due in the area within the hour.

She's landing! I've GOT to get some pictures of this!

Hold it right there, pal. You stay where you are until the army arrives!

But the troops weren't the only ones to arrive.

Keep those crowds back! Move the troops all around that thing—cover it with every weapon we have! MOVE!

Hallo! If anyone aboard that craft speaks our language, let them answer now. We'll give you three minutes before we open fire!

And what happens if they don't understand?

We're not taking any chances. With the President due at any time, we can't risk alien attack. We're killing them as soon as they appear.

WHAT? You're crazy! They could be friendly—you must give them a chance to communicate first!

FOOTBALL MAGIC

TOWNCASTER VILLA were a highly successful English First Division team, joint top of the league—

FLYING FURY

Start pumping! Hurry! Our planes depend on that fuel.

Jerry's bound to come over. He seems to know our every move.

DURING World War II, the island of Malta was taking a terrific pounding from the Germans. Flying with the island's Hurricane Squadron, was Sergeant Fury, a deadly pilot who flew like a man who knew no fear.
In the Grand Harbour—

A German air armada was on its way.

Our radio plane will give the directions. Bomb-aimers stand by.

Suddenly.

Let's go!

Fury was right about the time. He's uncanny.

Sergeant Fury led the attack.

That one's not going to make it!

Gott in Himmel . . . !

The bombers know exactly where the tanker is—yet they can't possibly see it!

Run! Run for your lives. We've been hit!

Use the foam pumps!

Fury's downed another! We caught 'em napping. Maybe the tanker can still be saved!

Flight Commander Bill Tomlinson was astonished . . .

Fury's breaking off the fight! What's going on? He's not the kind of man who runs!

Back at Z squadron base.

It's Sarge Fury! He must be hit!

His kite looks all right. Why has he come back?

Fury! Wait! What's wrong?

No time for a chat!

Hey, that's my machine! Stop!

Look at that sergeant! He's going like crazy—and there are flak splinters everywhere!

He's down! He's done for!

But then . . .

Hey, look! He's from the mo'bike crash.

He's going aboard the blazing tanker!

He's going below deck—what's he up to?

He'll be killed! That's for sure!

73

The ship can be saved. I managed to get the foam extinguisher lines working . . . Carry on.

I don't believe it! He came out of that alive!

Later.

Look out . . . ! It's that crazy sergeant again!

I thought he'd wrecked himself—and the bike!

There's something strange about that guy. How could he survive?

Meanwhile, in a side-street . . .

I left the transmitter in the tanker's hold. The beam signal would have been picked up by the master radio plane.

Then what went wrong? How come the tanker survived?

Both men were enemy agents.

Someone coming! We daren't be seen together. I'll plant the transmitter myself next time!

74

You in the arch—I know you're there! I know about your radio transmitter!

Heil Hitler! You have sentenced yourself to death!

Somehow, I think not!

The spy's gun spoke first.

Later . . .

He was a spy! He fired first! He missed—I didn't!

You can't prove that, sergeant. Until the spy charge is proved, you're under arrest!

At Z squadron H.Q.

Do we have to do this, sir? We need Fury in the air!

I know it—but we can't make exceptions! Somehow, we have to prove it was a spy he killed!

Next morning . . . at the docks.

Did you hear about the spy getting shot?

Yes and I hear they've arrested an air force sergeant.

At Z squadron base.

Fury, I'm sorry about the cell but that's how it has to be!

Not to worry! I won't be here much longer!

There were two spies! The other one got away!

I only wish we could prove it!

Will it mean a court of enquiry, sir?

It has to! Sergeant Fury's grounded until he's been cleared! Yet we need every flier!

76

He's stabbed the sergeant!

You won't stop me!

The knife missed! Something deflected it! He's the other spy! The partner of the man who was shot!

UUGH!

I'm sure he was stabbed—but, no, he can't have been . . .

I suggest we use the transmitter for a trap of our own! Listen . . .

A little later.

The cell's empty! Fury's escaped!

He can't have! How could he have got past us?

The C.O. was on the phone.

A spy caught? By an R.A.F. sergeant?

Sir, Sergeant Fury's missing! But the cell's still locked!

In Fury's cell.

Sergeant Fury . . . ?

Anything the matter, sir? Have you come to tell me news?

Good show! Fury's been cleared!

The second spy was caught red-handed and confessed.

Were you the mysterious sergeant who caught the spy, and then disappeared?

How could I be? I was in my cell. There's been some kind of mix-up.

That night, Nazi bombers from Sicily homed on to the " Spy " signal.

Follow this course! I'll give you the readings for your bomb-sights!

But.

Here they come!

Straight to us. Fire! Fire!

It's a trap! Flak ships . . . waiting for us!

Our agents have betrayed us!

Sergeant Fury led the night fighter attack.

Tally-ho! Now we wipe them out!

Fury's deadly! He never misses!

After this, Jerry won't be so keen on spy transmitters.

We socked it to 'em.

They've had a basinful. They're running for home!

Back at Z squadron.

I'm just making sure you hadn't vanished—again—Fury!

You get the funniest ideas! Too much imagination! That's your trouble!

The End

CORKS — WHAT A DUEL!

In 1808, an amazing duel took place over Paris. The two opponents were in balloons and with a blast from a blunderbuss, each man tried to puncture the other's gasbag. The duel ended when one of the balloons was pierced and the duellist plunged to his death.

The longest duel on record lasted for a mammoth 19 years! It was between a famous French duellist, Fournier, and a Captain Dupont, of Napoleon's army. Whenever one of them was wounded, they would declare the contest a draw. After 19 years they called a truce!

When an argument developed between two Oxford students, a duel seemed the only way to settle it. So, taking five paces, they turned and fired—champagne corks!

High on the list of weird duels was the one between an American general and an English officer. They agreed to sit on gunpowder barrels and light the fuses. The American stayed on longer —only because he knew the barrels were empty!

Two Brazilian footballers had a duel on motor cycles. Pistols in hand, they raced toward each other blazing away. One rider was hit and taken to hospital with a serious bullet wound!

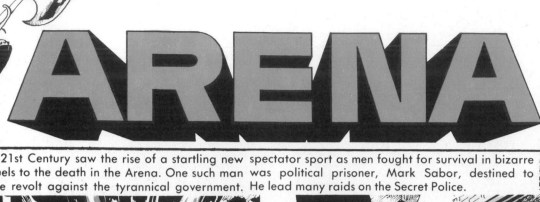

ARENA

THE 21st Century saw the rise of a startling new spectator sport as men fought for survival in bizarre duels to the death in the Arena. One such man was political prisoner, Mark Sabor, destined to lead the revolt against the tyrannical government. He lead many raids on the Secret Police.

AIEEEE!

Minutes later—

We hit them pretty hard tonight, Sabor!

Maybe. But each mission means the odds are stacked higher against us. The Secret Police aren't fools, and they are determined to crush us.

Soon, they reached the airshaft that took them back into the Arena—

But when you fight to free your countrymen from the cruel grip of the corrupt government you don't expect it to be easy.

No, but it's a fight we will win, Mark. We have to!

All clear. Return to your cells, men and get some rest. You did well.

Several days later, Deker, the Chief guard, watched Sabor and Varta sparring—

AAAH! Good hit, Mark!

Ha. A gap in your defence, Varta. You'll have to be more careful!

You've proved your point, Mark. Ach. I smell something foul. It's Deker, King Rat of this accursed place.

And a man determined to see me dead, by whatever means he can. I wonder what he wants?

85

The End

POP LOLLY

POP LOLLY, the school crossing man with the magic lolly, was at work, when—

"Look out, Tommy!"

"Gee, thanks, Pop. That was close. You lifted me up just in time!"

"The maniac! He should be arrested for driving like that!"

"Thank goodness you were here, Pop. We can always depend on you and your magic lolly."

Later—

"So long, kids. See you at teatime."

"See you, Pop."

Meanwhile, in town.

"It's a big haul. Let's get out of here, quick!"

"Step on it, Hank. The cops are after us."

"Don't worry. They won't catch us!"

"It's that fool of a lollipop man again! Serves him right."

BAM!

YIKES!

The pursuing police car swerved to avoid Pop Lolly.

"Oo—my head!"

SCREECH!

CRUMP

That's torn it. The robbers will get clean away.

No, they won't, gents. Just leave this to me.

What are you up to, Pop?

No time to explain . . .

I . . . I see it but I don't believe it! He must be travelling at eighty miles an hour!

Hey! Here comes that lollipop bloke again!

He . . . He's catching up!

AAARGH! Look out, Hank! A corner!

He's caused all the trouble. Blast 'im!

If there's blasting going to be done around here, I'm the one that's going to do it!

. . . 9 . . . 10 and out! Game's over, gentlemen!

UNNGHH!

Three hours later, Pop was back at his post—

That's the job I'm going to have when I leave school!

Why?

'Cos you don't have to start till you're sixty-five! Ha! Ha!

The End

90

91

I'm not leaving this ship! And neither are you!

You're a big bloke, Jan—but SLOW!

That blow should have put him out but it hasn't had the slightest effect!

I'll try a drop-kick! Ah, he's stunned himself on that pillar!

UNGH!

Okay, Jan—TALK! Where did you get the watch you sold to Art Lancey?

I found the policeman's body and took his watch. I DID NOT KILL HIM! But I saw three men leave. One of them had a shotgun— and he only had three fingers on his left hand!

THE JOLLY DOCKER

Crag went looking for a lead—

Ben Copping's the only man I know with two fingers missing from his left hand. And it was Pop Wilcox who had him put away for ten years! This is Sid the Snout's haunt—he might be able to tell me where Ben and his brothers live these days.

Inside—

You've been lucky so far, Sid! How long do you think I can keep missing your ugly mug?

No, please! No more!

Suddenly—

Outside, Sid! I want a word with you!

Th—thanks, Mr Crag.

URGH!

It didn't take Crag long to find Copping's flat—

Outside—

The Copping brothers? They've got a flat in Cresnall Gardens—number thirty-three! But be careful—I hear Ben's got a shotgun!

CRAG!

Unfortunately they don't hang cop-killers any more, but by the time I'm finished with you three you'll wish they did!

I'LL GET YOU, CRAG! You ain't takin' me in! That stupid copper shouldn't have got in my way!

You always were an idiot, Ben! You've wasted two barrels with the one shot!

And you two ain't big enough to beat me!

AGH! MY KNEE!

96

KING COBRA

BILL KING, world-roving reporter, was among newsmen gathered at the Niagara Entry Port when big-time gangster Lew "Tomatoes" Tomassin arrived for deportation to the United States.

Hey, Tomatoes! Is it true you're turning informer on the crime syndicate?

Back off, boys. Make way.

Bill phoned the newspaper editor he was working for . . .

The Mounties are rushing him straight through, sir. No chance of an interview.

King, a good reporter makes his own chances. Get in there.

Suddenly . . .

Something's happening. Excuse, me.

Must be some kind of knock-out gas.

Bill's special suit held many surprises, for Bill was no ordinary reporter . . .

Lucky I carry my own air supply.

The Mounties—but no sign of Tomatoes! Well, there's only one way he could have gone . . .

NIAGARA ENTRY

PORT

There he is. Tomatoes has been snatched.

Bill's car was handy . . .

The snatchers are turning on to the multi-lane towards Fort Erie.

Now they're turning off.

They're taking that dirt road down to the river. I'll park here.

98

99

101

THE END

The WRECK THAT WENT RIGHT

BRAD JONES and Greg Roberts, ex-Royal Navy frogmen, ran a business called Underwater Unlimited. They would go anywhere, tackle any job that involved diving. When the small oil tanker "North Rose" ran aground several miles off the port of Midhaven, a number of tugs tried in vain to salvage her. Then Jed Fellows, an old shipmate, called Brad and Greg in to help . . .

It's stuck mainly on the starboard side, at the stern. But we'll do a complete survey. That should help Jed.

That's that, and here comes Jed! Better get aboard!

It's stuck starboard—at the stern. If you want to try, Jed, we'll pass you a line.

Jed! Watch out! A monster wave—

The tug will be smashed to bits!

Those tugs are tough little craft, Greg.

Are you all right, Jed?

Radio's smashed, and the rudder control is damaged. I'll put into port for repairs and be back as soon as I can. Can you stay aboard?

Leave it to us, Jed. It will be your salvage while we're on board.

Jed steamed back to his base in Midhaven, where he met his great rival Red Rooney, who had already tried, unsuccessfully, to salvage the "North Rose."

Hey, Fellows! You'd some nerve trying to salvage that tanker when we had to pack it in. If Red Rooney can't salvage it—

Big-mouth! I've had it underwater surveyed and I'm going to have a go!

I've taken over all the local salvage firms apart from Fellows. I can't let him get away with this! I'll fix him.

Rooney got on the phone.

According to Mr Rooney, the top salvage expert on that coast, there's no hope of saving the tanker. That means thousands of tons of oil on our beaches. The oil must be destroyed.

Fleet Air Arm bombers are being loaded now, sir. They will drop high explosives, and then incendiaries to set the oil alight.

We've got to be sure there are no other vessels nearby.

We've sent a radio message to all nearby vessels. There was a tug there, but it's back in port. All is clear!

Five minutes later a flight of bombers took off, its target the "North Rose".

Look, Brad—the Fleet Air Arm is paying us a visit.

I wonder what they—oh no! Greg! They're going to bomb us!

Surely they can see there's someone aboard.

They probably can't make us out against the bulk of the tanker. Get to the top of the mast. They might spot us there.

Get up quick, Brad. Here comes the first bomber—

Wow! Those bombs were close! They'll get us with the next stick.

Old Joe's missed! But this one's going to be a bulls-eye!

Calling base. I can see two men on that ship!

Cancel attack immediately!

They got the message.

Hey, Greg—I think those bombs did some good. I felt the tanker shift slightly. Jed might be able to pull it clear after all!

But Jed was finding the going tough.

Sorry, Jed, I can't fix your rudder gear. I've got to finish work on one of Mr Rooney's tugs first. I've got a contract with him.

But I can salvage that tanker, if only I can get my tug going!

Get under way. We're going to the North Rose again. Fellows reckons he can get her clear, and if he can do it, so can we!

Here's Jed at last.

That's not Jed's tug. It's too big. It must be that guy Rooney Jed was telling us about.

107

That'll keep them out.

Think you're safe down there, do you? The ship's plates are sprung and water will come in. You won't get out—we're locking the hatch from this side!

Meanwhile, Greg had reached Midhaven.

The water's rising quicker than I thought—but my oxygen will keep me going for a while.

You've got to get there quickly, Jed. Brad can't hold out on his own for long.

I can't get anyone to fix my rudder gear. All the marine engineers are owned by Rooney, and they won't help.

See—the part that's broken works on the same principle as a bicycle chain—and you know how to fix one of them.

Yes, that seems simple enough . . .

Greg took a look at the gear, raced to a nearby cycle shop, picked up the owner and brought him back to the tug.

Meanwhile, back at the North Rose.

She's moving slightly—but we don't know exactly where she's caught on the rocks.

I've got to get clear before my air gives out. Hey! These plates are springing wider. If Rooney keeps pulling, he might make a hole wide enough for me to get through.

Thanks, Rooney—I might just do it now.

Rooney doesn't know I'm free. How can I delay him until Jed gets here? I'll get aboard the tanker and snoop around.

These bolt-cutters could be handy. Now where does the tow-line come aboard?

There it goes, like a bullet—and that gives me an idea for when they put a new line on!

Brad slipped into the water while Rooney and his men fixed a new tow-line. When the tug started heaving again . . .

The line is under maximum strain now—and should be in the right position for me! Here goes!

The released towline crashed into the stern of the tug like a shell.

The line's gone again! It's hit the rudder!

Stop engines! The screw is jammed!

My rope trick worked—and here comes a squall! The tug will be helpless in these seas, with no power and no steering.

The ship is waterlogged, boss! It'll turn over any minute!

Man the lifeboat! Let's get out of here!

111

At last the other tug hove in sight.

Can you tow her in this weather, Jed?

We're going to try!

Using the information Brad and Greg had obtained from their underwater survey, Jed was finally able to pull the North Rose clear.

Back in Midhaven.

You've had trouble, Mr Rooney.

That tanker would break anyone's heart. It's on the rocks for keeps.

What do you mean? It's heading into the harbour now!

So, Fellows, you're an expert now, having salvaged one ship, eh!

Not just one, Rooney—

We picked up your tug, too, Rooney—and we're going to nail you for salvage money!

But don't worry. I can recommend a very good bicycle-dealer who'll have your tug ship-shape in no time!

THE END

112

The Mill Street Mob

Five-a-side football—and Sep Manson scores for Mill Street School.

The week before, Sep and Kenny Grant met outside a High Street Sports shop.

SCHOOLS FIVE-A-SIDE SOCCER
FIFTY POUNDS
FOR WINNING TEAM
ONE TEAM FROM EACH SCHOOL
ENTER NOW!

Hey, let's go in for that, Kenny! That's ten quid's worth of gear each if we win!

Fatty will play, and Colin Turner! And Ginger Jackson . . . that's our five! Let's get our entry in.

Two other Mill Street boys, Knocker White and Buster Barnes, wanted to enter teams.

You play Sep Manson's kids, Knocker . . . and the winner plays my lot—see who represents Mill Street.

I can beat Sep Manson's mob without playing them. Take the notice down . . . I'll do a new one.

5-A-SIDE FOOTBALL
BARNES' FIVE
V
WHITE'S FIVE
TONIGHT
IN THE GYM

H

Knocker White's notice was pinned on the board.

We're not playing tonight, then, Sep.

We'll play the winners the day after! Give us more time to practise, won't it?

What'll happen to 'em if they don't turn up tonight?

FIRST XI

They'll be disqualified! Just be between your team and mine now!

A senior boy had volunteered to referee the game.

Where's Sep Manson's team, then?

They pulled out! Frightened we'd beat 'em . . . So we'll have to play Buster's lot to settle who represents Mill Street.

The game started.

Don't let him beat you . . . nobble him!

G-O-OA-LL!

Buster's team quickly scored three more goals.

FOUR-NIL . . . and we've only been playing five minutes! You're USELESS, mate!

Yeah! An' YOU'RE all MOUTH, Knocker White!

If you were any good you'd be scoring at the other end.

Ohhh!

Give me the ball, Buster. I'll knock in another while these two are busy.

Hey . . . you can't do that!

G-O-OA-LL!

Next moment.

Arrrghh!

Stop! I'm disqualifying the lot of you! Pack it up!

Gerrof me!

Sep and Kenny's team had been practising in the Town Hall. As they left—

Colin, you clumsy nit!

It don't half hurt. I-I think it's busted!

Looks a bit funny, don't it? Let's get him to a doctor . . .

Later.

How is he? Hey, looks bad—

Busted his wrist . . . there goes our goal-keeper!

DR. D.P. DANIE
SEN. PAN.
DR. L.W. SELY
PEDIATRICIAN.

The boys walked home through the park.

They're Mill Street School girls, aren't they?

Good save that. Vera Brown's in the Fifth form at Mill Street School.

Got a good throw too. Look at that! Not bad, for a girl!

The following day, at school.

Why didn't your team turn up at the five-a-side game last night, Sep?

We weren't playing, Mr Troy. We practised in the Town Hall. Who won last night?

You should have been playing! I wrote out the fixtures myself!

That's not what the notice said, sir.

Let's go and get it . . .

"There you are. Barnes' side plays White's side!"

"You've been tricked, but both White's team and Barnes' team were disqualified! So you go into the Finals! You're the only Mill Street team left!"

"YIPPPPPEEE!"

"Snag is . . . we ain't got a goalie now that Colin's busted his wrist!"

"I've got an idea—Follow me!"

"You want me to play in five-a-side football? That's a boys' game!"

"There's nothing in the rules that says a girl can't play."

"And we'll practise a bit and show you the game."

"All right! I'll play! Be a giggle, won't it?"

"Smashing!"

On Saturday afternoon, Mill Street played their way to the Final.

"Come on, Sep . . . you're one down. It's nearly time!"

"Bung it out, Vera. We gotta go!"

Great throw!

Have a go, Kenny!

G-O-OA-LL! Three-all!

The match was decided on penalty kicks. Each player shot in turn.

Great goal, Fatty! That's five to us!

An' they've got four! It all depends on their last shot!

I can't watch!

If Vera lets this one in, I suppose we just carry on until someone misses.

You've had it Vera! You never even saw the first four shots. Serves you right for playin' a girl, Grant!

You shut up, Knocker. Just because you—

THE END

NO CHRISTMAS DINNER for the CONQUERORS

C'mon, Beefy! There's a war on—and we've got work to do!

Won't be a moment, Paddy! Just giving Cookie a hand with the Christmas grub.

DURING World War II, the RAF's 1066 Squadron, known as the Conquerors, was based on a Dutch airstrip, helping to push back the Germans. But uppermost in Flying Officer "Beefy" Bailey's mind was his Christmas dinner!

Bags of grub there, mate! We're gonna have a real Christmas spread this year!

You're always thinking of food, Beefy. Hurry up, it's time for us to get cracking!

The Thunderbolts took off—

Scratch that train! That's one railway engine that won't go anywhere!

Soon, just outside the village of Vendhoven—

Target ahead, Conquerors! Follow me in—and good luck!

We have saved many British and American flyers who are passed through our "pipeline" as we call it. Everyone in Vendhoven is happy to help the escape route. Ah! A knock at the door!

Carrots Barton and Paddy Flood! So you were shot down too!

Yeah! But the villagers found us before the Jerries did!

Next day, in the village square, the dreaded Colonel Dollund, the local chief of the Gestapo, addressed the villagers—

Citizens of Vendhoven, deliver up the British flyers! You cannot get them out! The village is surrounded!

If these airmen are not surrendered to me immediately, all food supplies in the village and surrounding farms will be seized. We will starve you to your senses!

Dollund means what he says.

Later, Johannes explained the situation to the three flyers—

We can't let your people starve because of us! We'll make a break for it tonight!

You'll be caught at once! Dollund has the village sealed off! Anyway, our people would rather starve than help the Germans!

It'll soon be Christmas and we wouldn't like your people, especially the children, to have a miserable Christmas because of us!

Think nothing of it! Most families in the village have been putting away a little meat, sausage and so on especially for Christmas. We'll get by!

Meanwhile, the Germans were searching Vendhoven—

Achtung! Open up!

To prevent the airmen being smuggled into a house that had already been searched, Dollund posted a guard at each house, as it was cleared. Johannes held an emergency meeting in the cellar—

We'll have to get you out tonight, before the search reaches this end of the village! Wear these civilian clothes I've brought you! Here is what we're going to do . . .

That night—

There is a chance that this road may not be closely guarded.

Out of luck! Not unexpected! We'll have to try the fields!

But, in the fields—